Welcome to the deep dark wood!

Do you know who all of these characters are? Can you colour them in?

"The Big Bad Mouse is terribly strong
And his scaly tail is terribly long.

His eyes are like pools of terrible fire
And his terrible whiskers are tougher than wire."

Can you complete the pictures and colour them in?

THE GRUFFALO'S CHILD
COLOURING BOOK

Coloured in by

....

Julia Donaldson   Axel Scheffler

MACMILLAN CHILDREN'S BOOKS

The Gruffalo said that no gruffalo should
Ever set foot in the deep dark wood.

Can you draw your own Big Bad Mouse?

The snow fell fast and the wind blew wild.
Into the wood went the Gruffalo's Child.

Colour in the picture and add some snow.

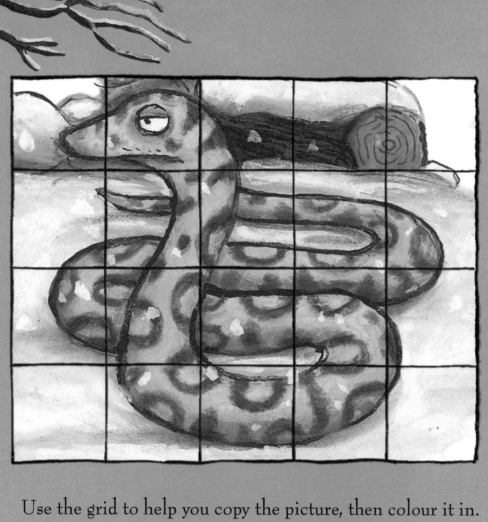

Use the grid to help you copy the picture, then colour it in.

Owl lives in a treetop house. Can you think of any other animals which live in trees? Add them to this picture and colour it in.

What do you think it looks like inside Owl's house?
Draw it in, or try sticking in some pictures.

Out slunk the creature. His eyes weren't fiery.
His tail wasn't scaly. His whiskers weren't wiry.

Who could the creature be?
Join the dots to find out, then colour in the picture.

Look, a snowman! Can you draw his face and decorate him before he melts?

Use the grid to help you copy the picture, then colour it in.

These animals also live in the deep dark wood.
Can you add some more forest creatures, then colour in the picture?

Aha! Oho! A trail in the snow!
Whose is this trail and where does it go?

Can you add in the trails, then colour in each animal?

Out came the moon. It was bright and round.
A terrible shadow fell onto the ground.

Can you draw the terrible shadow, then colour in the picture?

Who is that hanging from the hazel tree?
Join the dots to find out, then colour in the picture.

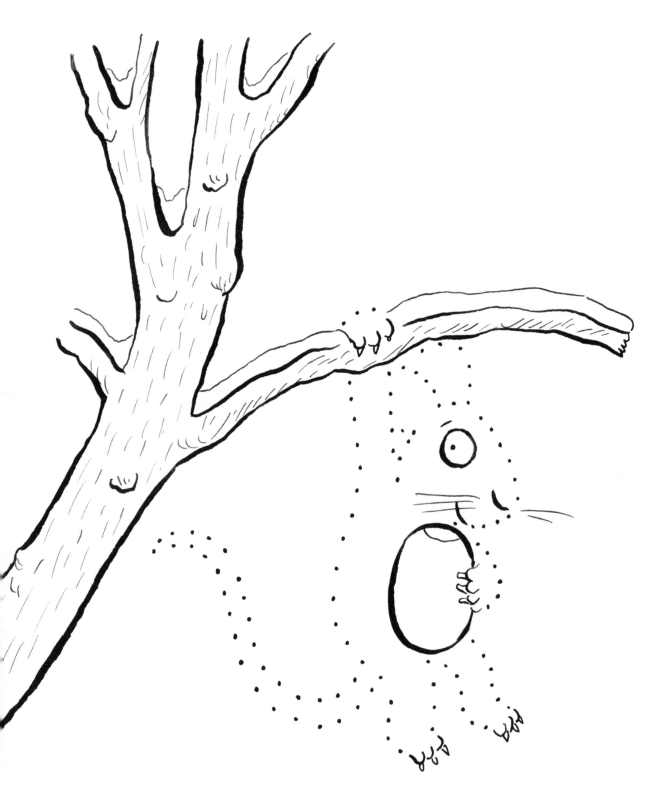

"The Big Bad Mouse!" yelled the Gruffalo's Child.
The mouse jumped down from the twig and smiled.

The Gruffalo's Child is hungry. Can you draw her a midnight feast and colour it in?

What is in the Gruffalo's cave?
Can you complete the pictures and colour them in?

What else would you find in the Gruffalo's cave?
Draw them in here or try sticking in some pictures.

Can you draw some pictures on the cave wall and colour in the picture?